Hello, Beach
Hola, playa

by Deborah Sc...

T0298242

ISBN: 978-1-338-70282-8
Illustrated by Anne Kennedy
Copyright © 2020 by Deborah Schecter. All rights reserved.
Published by Scholastic Inc., 557 Broadway, New York, NY 10012

10 9 8 7 6   68   23 24 25 26/0

Printed in Jiaxing, China. First printing, June 2020.

Hello, sun.

Hola, sol.

Hello, sand.

Hola, arena.

Hello, shell.

Hola, caracola.

Hello, crab.

Hola, cangrejo.

Hello, gull.

Hola, gaviota.

Hello, sail.

Hola, velero.

Well, hello, WHALE!

Bueno… ¡hola, BALLENA!